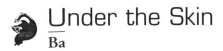

for return on or befc

HEDGE HOPPING

and other plays

Rob Brannen

Contents:

Under the Skin - *The Plays:*

Book 1: Louise Loxton Night Caller, The Gift, Boys Behaving Badly, Sleeping Easy, Bath Time

Book 2: Mike Gould Ring of Blood, Animal Magic, Eco-freaks in Trouble, The Case of the Following Boy, The Sub

Book 3: Rob Brannen Hedge Hopping, Sorting Things Out, Michael and Rahima, Into the Dark, A Swagger and A Snarl

Book 4: Mike Gould Ten Things I Hate, Joker in the Pack, Dial-a-date, Masked Ball, The First Girl in Space

Book 5: Dick Kempson Conquistador, The Boy at the Hotel Rudolpho

Book 6: Mike Gould Ice Maiden, Under the Skin

Badger Publishing Limited 15 Wedgwood Gate, Pin Green Industrial Estate, Stevenage, Hertfordshire SG1 4SU
Telephone: 01438 356907.   Fax: 01438 747015.
www.badger-publishing.co.uk   enquiries@badger-publishing.co.uk

Under the Skin - Book 3   ISBN 978 184424 430 0

Text © Rob Brannen 2005
Series editing © Mike Gould 2005
Complete work © Badger Publishing Limited 2005

Series Editor: Mike Gould   Publisher: David Jamieson
Editor: Paul Martin   Cover design: Adam Wilmott
Cover illustration: Milivoj Ceran (Beehive Illustration)

Introduction

Welcome to Badger's *Under the Skin* Book 3!

This collection of five stimulating and challenging plays is designed for enjoyment, but also to help students develop speaking and listening, drama and theatre skills. The series title also gives a clue to the focus for these plays. They may cover a range of ideas, issues, stories and situations, but each is intended to uncover how and why individuals act in the way they do. Thus, these are plays designed with the stage and acting in mind, though they can be equally enjoyed as group readers.

The plays themselves offer a mix of humour and emotion, joy and sadness, triumph and despair, and also cover a wide range of forms and styles. In particular, this collection offers students the chance to explore the full range of dramatic action and performance as they take on a wide variety of roles (often at the same time!).

The plays range from the reflective and moving two-hander, *Sorting it Out*, to the positive thrust of *Michael and Rahima,* which pitches a comfortably-off teenage boy in the UK on the opposite side of the stage - and the world - from Rahima, eldest daughter of a poor family working on the tea crop. The plays change focus again with the humour and energy of the group dramas, *Hedge Hopping* and *Into the Dark,* both ideal for group reading and especially performance. Finally, the darker *A Swagger and a Snarl* ends the collection - providing a prologue for other plays in the series such as *Under the Skin* and *Conquistador* (both found in the next level).

All the plays in the series are written by people who are involved, or have been involved, in practical drama work with young people aged 11-16. For this reason, it is hoped that teachers and students will find them compelling and rewarding.

HEDGE HOPPING

Characters:

DEN

HACKER

CJ

MAD MATT   boys, all about 13

Three boys run into the space one at a time - breathless.

DEN: Den home! One!

HACKER: Hacker home!

DEN: Two!

CJ: CJ home!

DEN: Three!

There is a pause. They look anxiously off. Suddenly MAD MATT runs on...

MATT: (*breathless*) Mad Matt well and truly home!

DEN: Four!

They begin to congratulate each other, deep-breaths and smiles. They break into a ritual which involves hand-gestures and synchronised movement.

ALL: We run, we climb
We're home in good time
There's no way of stopping
The best
The best
The best at hedge hopping
The best at hedge hopping
THE BEST at hedge hopping!

More congratulations. Then they turn to the audience and DEN speaks. They are still trying to catch their breath as they speak.

DEN: This is what we do. The art of hedge hopping.

CJ: The ancient art...

HACKER: The noble art...

MATT: It is just the best, it's hysterical, you should see these guys, we have had some brilliant times I can tell you and I mean brilliant...

DEN: As I was saying, this is what we do... tell 'em, CJ.

CJ: First you've got to pick a run...

MATT: Crucial...

CJ: (*slightly annoyed at MATT*) Which is crucial. Your run is like the course. It's where you start and where you finish and everything that happens in between.

DEN: And what happens in between is gardens and hedges.

HACKER: Or fences.

DEN: Yeah, hedges or fences.

MATT: Anything you can climb over, jump over, dive through...

CJ: So you start in the street and you climb the first fence, say, and then you run through the garden to the next and carry on like that - run and over... run and over...

DEN: Sometimes stopping to give a bunk-up...

MATT: Which is like this...

He demonstrates with HACKER - cupping his hands so that HACKER can get a foot-hold in them and then a boost up high. They make a mess of it and fall in a heap.

             ...only better.

CJ: Then there are hedges that you have to 'hop'...

DEN: CJ's got the best technique.

CJ: Well, actually it's best to kind of dive and roll over the top and back onto your feet on the other side. (*he demonstrates the technique as he tells the audience*)

DEN: Or, if you're Hacker, who is the best at all things computerish - websites, megabytes, that sort of thing... but not... what can I say? ...the most sporty of us... then you don't really get over the hedges... you run straight through 'em.

MATT: (*laughing whilst HACKER is looking sheepish*) Yeah, straight through 'em or find a little gap at the bottom you can squeeze through and end up with twigs and leaves and all that in your hair and clothes and coming out of your ears and all that...

CJ: Or, if you're Mad Matt, you can try to do the high jump like in the athletics...

HACKER: The Fosbury Flop.

MATT: I saw it on the telly, didn't I... thought I'd give it a go.

DEN: He flopped all right. Right on his fosburies.

MATT: No crash-mat the other side was there... forgot about that.

CJ: So, anyway, you go over however many there are in the run and then you end up back in the street further down. The average run will have... (*he thinks for a moment*) ...about five gardens.

9

HACKER: But our record is eight.

MATT: Nine!

DEN: It was eight, Matt, you weren't counting properly.

The others agree.

MATT: Nine... definitely nine...

HACKER: Eight, Matt, you moron, because we told you that my garden doesn't count. (*explaining to the audience*) That time... the record-breaking time... we ended up finishing the run in my garden...

DEN: That was 'home'.

MATT: Hacker's home was 'home'... but it was his home not my home, so it counts for me and not for him. So it's nine.

DEN: All right, just leave it.

HACKER: That day was our 'Grand National'. But we can't do it again.

DEN: Because some of Hacker's neighbours got upset...

CJ: For good reason...

DEN: It wasn't so much the trespassing which was the problem... but an incident with a pond and Mr Risebrow's Koy Carp.

They all turn to look at MATT, who looks the other way.

     Somebody thought it would be funny to go through the water rather than round.

They look at MATT again.

     It was like this...

They all move into position and re-enact the event. MATT is running in to catch up and the others are all climbing over a fence ahead. They show in slow motion.

MATT: Wait for me lads!

HACKER: CJ, give me a bunk-up, I can't reach.

DEN: Matty - mind the pond! (*to the audience again*) ...and somebody caused such a splash...

MATT: (*as though running through the pond - in slow motion he shows each wet step*) Ker-splish! ...Ker-splosh! ...Ker-splash!

11

MATT: (*he shows with hand gestures the direction the fish fly in*) Carp! ...Carp! ...Carp!

HACKER: Enormous fish flapping around the garden...

The others snap into real-time as they run around trying to catch and hold the fish. MATT stands stunned.

...we managed to put two of them back but then Risebrow came out of his shed waving a spade like a mad axe-man.

MATT: (*becoming the angry neighbour*) Mad Spade-man! (*demonstrates to the audience*)

ALL: (*freezing in a tableau. MATT as threatening Spade-man, the others trying to escape*) Aaaaaaaaahhhhh!!!! (*it is frozen for a moment and then all snap out of it, to talk to the audience*)

CJ: That's the thing you see, the gardens are obviously not our gardens... which makes it dangerous and exciting...

HACKER: And probably illegal.

Pause.

DEN: Breath back?

The others nod.

DEN: Hacker?

HACKER: Yeah.

DEN: Are you sure?

HACKER: (*nods*) Sure.

DEN: We've just had a practice on a short run. Because today... today we go for the record...

CJ: We've found a new run...

HACKER: We did our homework on it... a combination of fences and hedges... different heights... enough of a challenge... CJ could look over all the gardens from his Nan's loft conversion.

MATT: No ponds.

CJ: We hope.

Pause. They look at him.

Well, I couldn't see everything.

13

DEN: Ten gardens… connecting two parallel streets. We're going for the record… (*to the audience*) Do you want to come?

They turn around to indicate change of time and place. They prepare for the challenge by limbering up.

CJ: OK, now from what I could see from Nan's window, there's this first fence here which needs a bunk up for the first three and the last man will need a pull up from the other side. Then there's a low fence, then a hedge - medium height - followed by a row of conifer fir trees - so look for the gaps. Then there's three low walls which should be easy. Then four more gardens before we're home.

HACKER: Fences or hedges?

CJ: I don't know, do I? I told you I couldn't see everything. If I'd have leaned out of that window any more I would have fallen down into Nan's garden.

MATT: Splat! Dead on the decking. He he he.

HACKER: Could be anything then.

CJ: What?

HACKER: There could be anything in those four gardens - barbed wire, trenches...

CJ: Barbed wire?

HACKER: It's a risk, CJ. We don't know the run, it's broad daylight on a sunny day, so there's bound to be people about. Remember the Mad Spade-man.

DEN: Risk's good. It's what we do.

MATT: And don't forget the new rule.

DEN: Yeah, one item collected from each garden, named as a challenge by one of the others. Matt collects first...

MATT: Not something big like a birdtable or something... I'm not nicking a birdtable...

DEN: No it has to fit in your pocket... like we agreed. Matt, then Hacker, then CJ, then me. We have two goes each and then the last two gardens we all have to take something.

HACKER: Take something?

DEN: Not stealing. Just... I don't know... a bit of grass or something.

MATT: Just for a laugh. A whatsit… a souvenir from each garden.

DEN: A collection of trophies from the day we broke the world record.

CJ: (*having doubts*) My nan lives round here.

DEN: Right. Everybody ready?

They brace themselves.

CJ, HACKER & MATT: Ready.

DEN: Matt, your first challenge is a twig from the first garden.

MATT: (*with great seriousness*) Challenge accepted.

DEN: Gentlemen, are we ready to take the record?

The others nod.

Then let's go!

All four break into action. During the hedge hopping sequence at times they run on the spot, sometimes freeze, sometimes move in slow motion, sometimes in real time. Hedges and walls can be mimed or tables and chairs used to represent them.

DEN: (*to the audience*) The first fence was high and really tricky. We helped each other, but it was a real scramble.

CJ: (*looking around*) Nobody about! Come on!

MATT: Got the twig!

HACKER: That's not a twig, that's half a tree, you nutter! Put it down!

ALL: Low fence! (*over they go*) Easy!

CJ: Hacker, get a flower.

HACKER: I will not!

CJ: Look, there's a dead one, there.

HACKER: Got it!

DEN: There's someone looking out the window. Move!

ALL: Hedge! (*over they go*) No problem!

DEN: (*looking quickly around*) Nobody about.

HACKER: CJ... one of those pebbles... over there.

CJ: Got it. Let's go! Let's go!

Their actions are suddenly slowed down as they tangle with...

ALL: Trees!

They fight and struggle their way through. HACKER is last to break through the tangle, pushing against the branches as he speaks. The others stand and stare at the sight which greets them in the next garden - forming a tight group.

HACKER: (*to the audience*) A row of really bushy conifer trees, scratching your arms and your face as we pushed, and struggled, and forced our way through to the next garden... (*he breaks through and joins the others*)

CJ: (*putting his hand over HACKER's mouth to stop him speaking, CJ whispers*) Where there is a lady...

DEN: (*whispers too*) ...sunbathing...

MATT: (*whispers too*) ...with a very small bikini on!

CJ: (*whispers too*) ...and her eyes closed.

They tip-toe past. MATT is trying not to look, then he remembers...

MATT: Den, your challenge should you choose to accept it. (*he signals towards the woman*) The sun-cream.

DEN looks terrified.

OK, OK, that dog chew, they must have a dog... the dog chew, there!

DEN: (*still whispering and tip-toeing*) Got it. Please, let's go.

Then they suddenly jump back to speed and volume, as DEN says to the audience...

The three low garden walls were dead easy. We collected... a feather! (*points and MATT collects*)

CJ: A scabby apple! There! (*HACKER collects*)

HACKER: That pine cone, there! (*CJ collects*)

DEN: Three more gardens to go...

CJ: ...and we beat the record!

ALL: Four foot fence!

MATT: Bit of a bunk up and we're over.

HACKER: (*to the audience*) Oh no! Old bloke gardening. Just standing there with his mouth open like this (*he illustrates*) ...and he says, "What the..." ...like this... "WHAT THE?!" ...and Matt says...

MATT: Would you like your car cleaning, Mister? Or what about some weeding? No? All right then, thank you very much. We'll try next door.

HACKER: And the bloke's still standing there with his mouth open as we climb over his fence.

ALL: (*as they go over*) Old bloke's fence!

DEN: Nobody in this garden.

HACKER: Are you sure?

CJ: Let's go! Let's go! He'll phone the police or something. Quick, come on!

ALL: Five foot wall! (*they are just about to go over*)

MATT: Wait a minute. Wait a minute! We didn't get anything. Not from the old bloke's garden and not from this.

CJ: Come on!

MATT: It's the rules. Den, it was your turn.

DEN: Come on, Matty. I'm not going back! Let's go! Let's go!

MATT: Next one's the last garden. You've got to get something good.

DEN: OK. Let's go!

MATT: Promise. Whatever I say.

DEN: OK, OK. Whatever. Move!

ALL: Five foot wall!

They get over and are immediately terrified by what's on the other side.

ALL: DOG!

HACKER: Oh no... a dog.

They make growling and barking sounds to illustrate.

CJ: A really big dog. Big teeth and everything...

DEN: Ferocious.

HACKER: We're dead. We're dog dinner. We're so dead.

They are slowly moving round the dog to get to the fence on the other side.

CJ: Why did we do this?

DEN: Lads, look.

HACKER: What?

DEN: Look at the wall. Our way to the street... the wall, there. Barbed wire... on the top... barbed wire.

Trapped, they look from one to the other, as they say...

ALL: Dog... Barbed Wire... Dog... Barbed Wire...

DEN: Gentlemen, it's a hedge hopper's nightmare.

MATT: Challenge.

DEN: Not now, Matt.

MATT: You said I could name anything. You promised. "Whatever," you said.

DEN: All right. All right. Name it.

MATT: The ultimate trophy. Dog collar.

DEN: Dog collar?!

ALL: (*trapped*) Dog... Barbed wire... Dog... Barbed wire...

DEN: ...nightmare.

They suddenly snap out of the scene and turn to the audience.

CJ: Well, shall we tell them?

HACKER: They did kind of come with us, didn't they.

MATT: It was glorious... magnificent... just.... brilliant... the best ever.

HACKER: Did we break the record?

CJ: Some big dog owner, with high-security barbed wire on his fence, only went out and left his side gate open, didn't he? Did we beat the record?

ALL: (*triumphant*) Yes!

They repeat the sequence from the beginning of the play.

ALL: We run, we climb
We're home in good time
There's no way of stopping
The best
The best
The best at hedge hopping
The best at hedge hopping
THE BEST at hedge hopping!

DEN: Oh, and did I win Matt's challenge? (*he produces a dog collar*) That big dog turned out to be a bit of a pussy cat. He really liked that dog chew, didn't he? Tried to look hard but really, honestly… just a big softy!

ALL: (*as they strike tough poses*) Yeah.

SORTING THINGS OUT

Characters:

NAT

MEL   sisters

NAT and MEL are in their bedroom. They speak to the audience.

NAT: We're sorting things out.

MEL: In our bedroom.

NAT: Because Mum told us to. She told us to sort out our bedroom because there are too many things in our cupboards and on the shelves, and under our beds and on our beds and in our beds. You need to sort things out, she said, but not in a calm way, in a screamy-mad-monster-from-hell way.

MEL: We've got to do it now because tomorrow is the School Fair.

NAT: And there's no putting it off any longer, it is time to decide what to keep and what to give to the School Fair.

MEL: And we're not allowed to buy it back again, or even think about entering the raffle in case we win something we just gave away.

NAT: So far I'm giving away some magazines, lipstick, a key-ring and a sing-a-long CD which we sometimes use as a Frisbee, so I don't think it plays very well anymore. But Mel can't really decide.

MEL: I hate it, I'd rather do Mr Gregson's Maths homework and I totally hate that.

NAT: What about this? (*she picks up something from one of the piles*)

MEL: No way, that's my favourite. It is, honestly.

NAT: We've been in here for ages and so far she's decided to give away this.

She holds up one small object.

MEL: Which my friend Rhiannon left here last week. The rest we've just kind of rearranged into lots of piles and thought about what it reminds us of and how much we'd miss it if it was gone.

NAT: Not that!

MEL: Not that!

BOTH: Definitely not that!

NAT: And Mum's going to go mad when she sees all the piles of stuff.

MEL: But I'm not going to give any of it away.

NAT: You could give your baby things away.

MEL: What baby things?

NAT: Like Mrs Loppy Rabbit.

MEL: Nat! How embarrassing! Don't you dare tell any of my friends.

NAT: Might, might not...

They glare at each other.

MEL: Grow up.

NAT: You grow up. You've got to choose something, I did.

MEL: You chose: a 10 piece jigsaw with 9 pieces, a key-ring from a Coco-pops packet and a CD that we once melted wax onto from my candle-making kit.

NAT: You could give away your candle-making kit.

MEL: Candles all made and melted.

NAT: Your make-your-own perfume set.

MEL: All sprayed away. Mostly by you!

NAT: Post office set.

MEL: All licked and sent. And I don't want to give away souvenirs or presents - it would be rude. You choose some more things, if you want to.

NAT: Yeah, you're right, it would be rude and everybody would think: 'I'm not going to give presents to Nat and Mel, because they'll only give them away.'

MEL: Yeah. What about the cheapskates' presents? That pile there is all the cheapskates' presents.

NAT: (*to the audience*) The cheapskates' presents are the presents that we opened on our birthday and Dad used to look over and say 'Cheapskates', which meant that he thought that the person who gave the present should have spent more money on it.

MEL: That was Dad being stupid, 'cause they were great things like glow felt-tips, or beads and elastic to make jewellery, or a packet of groovy-girl lick and stick tattoos.

NAT: (*being Dad*) Cheapskates!

MEL: Which is funny; because it was actually Dad who bought me a pair of cheap skates for my birthday, instead of the expensive ones I'd asked him for.

NAT: And the wheels kept on jamming and you kept falling down on your Arsenal tracksuit bottoms.

They laugh.

MEL: So I could give those skates away. (*pause*) Except... they are from Dad.

NAT: Dad's given us lots of presents recently. Mum doesn't like it. He sorted his things out very quickly.

MEL: What do you mean?

NAT: (*to the audience*) Dad came home one day and sorted his things out very quickly. Mum had gone to pick up Mel from Drama Club, and when she had gone Dad came home and said 'sorry' to me a lot. "Sorry Nat, I'm really sorry, Nat," he said. And I looked through the window and "That Woman" was sitting in his car, which is what Mum called her, but now we know she is called Liz and Dad lives with her not Mum.

So he came home in a hurry and cleared all the things from his side of the wardrobe and threw them in a case. Then he ran downstairs and I followed him.

30

NAT: And he started running his finger down his CD collection, saying "Come on, come on, where is it?" until his finger stopped and he found one CD and took it. It was one by a band called 'The Jam', who were before Destiny's Child or even before Robbie Williams started singing. I mean really old. It was the CD that he played and played and played, so he must have wanted to play it for "That Woman"... I mean Liz.

So I suppose he was better at sorting things out than us, 'cause he did it in the time it took Mum to pick up Mel. Some things from his wardrobe, some things from a drawer and one CD, and he was gone. There must have been nothing else here he wanted to take.

We should do that.

MEL: What?

NAT: Only keep the things that we really, really, really, I mean really want. The things that it would break our hearts to throw away, we keep, and all the rest we give to the school.

MEL: Right.

NAT: So, we'll just be brave and get one plastic bag each.

MEL: Right.

NAT: And when the bag is full of things we want to keep, all the rest goes.

MEL: Right.

NAT: OK. Here goes! Sorting things out quickly!

They look around the room, tortured by the decisions they are trying to make.

MEL: Now that is just the best. (*she puts it down again*)

NAT: This is a definite. (*she has second thoughts*) Maybe.

MEL: This! I couldn't live without this!

NAT: That's mine.

MEL: Oh, yeah.

This goes on for some time and their enthusiasm becomes less and less, until they give up.

I can't choose things to throw away and now I can't choose things to keep.

NAT: Sorting things out quickly doesn't work for us.

MEL: Nat?

NAT: What?

MEL: Do you think it worked for Dad?

NAT: Don't know.

MEL: (*to audience*) Gran was different. Gran sorted things out really slowly. We had to go to her old house to help.

NAT: When we got there we were so bored.

MEL: She wanted to take everything with her to her new flat.

NAT: Mum finally got her to move near to where we live. Because Gran was on her own, too far away and getting too old.

MEL: Now she lives in a shelter.

NAT: Very funny. She lives in sheltered accommodation, with a warden to look after her. But the old house, where Mum grew up, was full of things which needed sorting out.

MEL: And we sat on Gran's bed and she took a dress out of her wardrobe, very slowly, and held it up and said, "What about this one, girls?" and we said "Very nice, Gran" or "That really suits you, Gran," and she looked pleased and folded the dress really slowly and then took the next one out really slowly. Everything was so slow and quiet that I needed to go into the garden and run about and shout, so we did. And we played on the old swing for a bit but it started to get dark and we went back in.

Mum had been cleaning the kitchen when we went out, but Gran was in there now, wondering where all her tea towels had gone. She had 14 bottles of washing-up liquid under the sink. We went to find Mum, who was taking some of the dresses out of Gran's case and putting them in bin bags, with lots of tea towels and things.

MEL: "Look what I found," said Mum, and showed us books and toys from her room when she was little. There was a book about horses with lots of pictures; a tin with badges in; a doll called 'Daisy' that Gran had knitted for her...

NAT: How can you knit a doll?

MEL: She didn't put any of those things in the bin-bag, but in a box to take home.

Pause.

NAT: Mel, look! I've not seen this for ages! (*she picks up a toy*) Do you remember we bought this on holiday, when we stayed with Mum in a caravan? First time without Dad. She got cross 'cause she didn't want us to buy it.

MEL: And it was too much money, so we said we would buy it together and Mum said it was still too much money. And we said "Please, please, please, Mum!" and we tried both tugging at her arms to show how much we wanted it, but it made her look cross.

NAT: So we tried the big eyes melt-her-heart look, like this. (*they both do the big eyes pleading 'look'*)

MEL: She started to smile.

NAT: And we said we'd go without pocket money for three weeks, and she said it was still too expensive and she'd buy us some popcorn.

MEL: And we said we'd go without birthday presents and Christmas presents.

NAT: And in the end she said 'yes'!

MEL: I wonder what it does?

NAT: I don't know, I've never played with it. Have you?

MEL: No.

NAT: Shall we give it away to the Fair?

MEL: No way.

MICHAEL & RAHIMA

Characters:

MICHAEL and RAHIMA   aged 14

PLAYER 1 and 2   narrators

MOTHER and FATHER   of both Michael and Rahima

This drama concerns the meeting of two worlds. At first, the worlds of Michael and Rahima are split, and then they cross the barrier between them. The staging should consider this, with an area for Michael's world and one for Rahima's. Player 1 and Player 2 position themselves on the appropriate sides as they narrate. The characters step forward, 'freeze' or step back, when required.

Note - 'Modern' references, such as the Girls Aloud *song and* Busted, *should be updated when necessary with appropriate equivalents.*

PLAYER 1: This is the story of Michael...

PLAYER 2: ...and Rahima.

MICHAEL: (*steps forward, introducing himself*) Michael.

He busies himself - checking in the mirror, opening draws, sniffing socks...

PLAYER 1: Michael, aged 14, woke to a world of internet, satellite, Game Boys and *Girls Aloud*. A world of CD ROM, remote control, mobile phones, instant credit, instant coffee, instant access to cruising the information superhighway.

MICHAEL: This morning he was having trouble instantly accessing a clean pair of socks whilst downloading his Kellogg's Multi-Grain Cheerios with added fibre.

RAHIMA: (*steps forward, introducing herself*) Rahima.

RAHIMA surveys the scene, fills a basin with water, washes and dresses, whilst Player 2 says:

PLAYER 2: Rahima, aged 14, woke to a world of silence and heat. Somewhere outside her village home in rural India, her father's chickens were clucking and scratching in the dust.

PLAYER 2: The hills in the distance were blanketed in green forest. She washed herself in a basin of water fetched from the village pump, and dressed herself in a sarong of purples and yellows.

PLAYER 1: Michael was still having trouble gelling his hair whilst watching *Busted* on breakfast telly.

MICHAEL: *Busted* - Breakfast telly...

RAHIMA: The forest - father's chickens...

MICHAEL: Changing channels - gelling hair...

RAHIMA: The village pump - the yellow and purple sarong...

PLAYER 1 & 2: Michael and Rahima were worlds apart.

MOTHER: Michael, you're late for school! Can't you hear your father revving?!

FATHER: (*mimes sitting revving the car*) Ruuuum. I'll swing for him. Ruuuummm. One of these days I'll go without him - I will. Ruuummm.

MOTHER: Michael, your father's exhaust fumes are becoming a health hazard!

PLAYER 1: Michael's parents say:

MOTHER: We understand teenagers, don't we, Brian?

FATHER: (*poor attempt to sing and dance a song*) I'll tell you what I want, what I really, really want...

BOTH: I wanna, I wanna, I wanna, I wanna... chinky, chinky boom-boom.

They both over-enjoy their 'pop routine'.

FATHER: Oh yes, we're very tolerant really. We don't mind if he has a healthy interest in Rachel Stevens.

MOTHER: We're just not sure if there is such a thing as a healthy interest in Rachel Stevens... Brian used to have a thing about Ginger Spice...

FATHER: (*embarrassed and coughing*) Thank you, Jean.

MOTHER: We know he's just going through one of those moody phases.

FATHER: Only it's lasted four and a half years now.

MOTHER: He only ever thinks about himself.

PLAYER 2: In India, Rahima is frustrated with her parents...

The focus shifts to RAHIMA's world.

RAHIMA: You treat me like a slave...

FATHER: I'm just saying we all have to lend a hand.

RAHIMA: But me more than most.

FATHER: You are the eldest.

RAHIMA: I work, the same as you, the same as my mother, but I have nothing to show for it.

PLAYER 2: So Rahima's father says:

FATHER: What do you want ?

RAHIMA: Just a little to buy the things I want.

FATHER: But we don't have a little to spare. Your wages help to cover the basics we need.

RAHIMA: It's not fair.

FATHER: No it's not fair. I know it's not fair. (*to audience*) What can we expect? She's 14 now. She works all day picking tea with her mother, she looks after her brothers and sisters, she helps in our home. (*pause*)

41

FATHER: I wish that her childhood had not been so short.

PLAYER 2: Rahima squats on the floor, rolling chapati dough, squashing it flat between the palms of her hands - tomorrow she will pick tea, and the day after, and the day after that...

PLAYER 1: Michael loads his school bag - perhaps he will go to university, get a flat, meet new friends.

BOTH: Worlds apart.

PLAYER 1: Then one day, something changed...

PLAYER 2: Michael read a book...

PLAYER 1: ...or perhaps he saw a programme...

PLAYER 2: ...or perhaps it was even something he heard at school...

PLAYER 1: And for the first time he heard about...

PLAYER 2: ...read about... He watched...

RAHIMA: Rahima working hard in the hot sun, constantly leaning forward, picking the fragile tea leaves...

RAHIMA & Rahima, squatting down making chapatis,
MICHAEL: looking after her brothers and sisters...

PLAYER 1: And as he read his book, or listened, or
watched...

MICHAEL: He imagined that he could speak to her...
really speak to her.

*They look at each other for the first time. Lots of shuffling
and awkwardness.*

RAHIMA: No longer worlds apart... an awkward
teenage first meeting...

MICHAEL: Through the magic that is drama...

*Confused/embarrassed - he can't quite believe what he
has just said.*

RAHIMA: What did you say?

MICHAEL: Nothing. It was nothing. I heard about you.
I think I read a book or watched a
programme or something, and I went into a
daydream and... here you are.

RAHIMA: How old are you?

MICHAEL: Fourteen. You?

RAHIMA: Fourteen too.

MICHAEL: Right. (*pause*)

RAHIMA: I pick tea...

MICHAEL: I drink tea... I... go to school.

RAHIMA: I never went to school.

MICHAEL: Lucky you.

RAHIMA: No, no, it's important...

MICHAEL: Only joking... He imagined how their stumbling conversation progressed.

RAHIMA: She told him how their village had started to change with the help of a Fair Trading Company...

MICHAEL: That's it! That's what I heard about.

PLAYER 2: As he read...

PLAYER 1: ...watched...

PLAYER 2: ...listened... Michael got to know Rahima and something happened, something highly unusual for Michael...

PLAYER 1: ...something of a little miracle.

PLAYER 2: He went out, with his own money, and when he returned home...

MOTHER: What are you doing skulking round the kitchen?

MICHAEL: (*giving her the packet*) I've bought some tea.

MOTHER: What's this?! We always get PG.

MICHAEL: It's Fairly Traded.

MOTHER: It's fairly expensive...

MICHAEL: I paid for it... you don't have to drink it... it's up to you... I'm going out.

MOTHER: Michael? Michael! (*he's gone*) What's he doing buying tea? I do the shopping - he's never even made a cup of tea.

MICHAEL: I know what you're thinking. OK, what difference does a box of tea make? But I bought a box of tea...

PLAYER 2: ...and Rahima said:

RAHIMA: Now there's a school in the village for my brothers and sisters.

MICHAEL: Mrs Bailey bought a box of tea...

RAHIMA: And now my mother can attend an Adult Literacy Group the company have set up.

MICHAEL: Mr Harvey, across the road, bought a box of tea...

RAHIMA: My wages have gone up from 13 rupees to 37 rupees a day.

MICHAEL: Mrs Mistry, who organises the tea and coffee in the staff room, bought 4 boxes...

RAHIMA: I now have a contract to protect my job.

MICHAEL: George Brooks, who's a real guzzler, bought 6 boxes in case he ran out...

RAHIMA: There is a 'Fair Price' shop where we can buy things cheaply.

MICHAEL: Dorothy, who likes it very weak, bought a box every six months...

RAHIMA: All my family live in one room. We are now saving for our own cottage.

She continues picking tea.

MICHAEL: Derek bought some tea. Nice Miss Hines, from the corner house, bought some tea. My friend Susan bought some tea. Old Ethel Slater bought some tea. My mum and dad even bought some tea, they said they'll get used to the taste. My mate Pete bought some tea. So Carol, who really likes Pete, bought some tea...

Michael fades his speech out to end the drama.

INTO THE DARK

Characters:

DREWEY	girl, aged 13
JESS	girl, also 13
DOM	boy, aged 13
WES	boy, also 13
KIA	Wes' sister, 11

The action is played out in an empty space with torches. Possibly some sleeping bags and what's left of a midnight feast. The action starts in a tent in WES and KIA's back garden. DREWEY is just finishing telling a ghost story.

DREWEY: And the next day she found an axe under the passenger seat, dripping with blood!

JESS: That's disgusting.

DOM: I feel sick. I feel sick now, I do.

WES: Do it outside the tent, Dom. If you don't mind. My parents would go mad if we messed it up.

KIA: Who's got the chocolate? I need to take the taste away.

WES: We've got chocolate, crisps, popcorn and some marshmallows left.

DOM: I'll have popcorn with marshmallows.

KIA: I thought you felt sick?

DOM: It's Drewey who is sick. Sick in the mind.

JESS: How do you make all those ghost stories up, Drewey?

DREWEY: I don't make them up...

ALL: They're true!

They all laugh.

DOM: I know ghost stories. Did you hear the one about the...

WES: Severed hand. Yeah, you told us before.

DOM: No. The one about the woman...

JESS: ...in Victorian times playing hide and seek in a big old house. And she can't find somewhere to hide, so she goes up into the attic room and quickly gets in an old trunk, like a big old Victorian chest, and the lid drops down. It's really heavy and rusted and much smaller in there than she had thought. Now she can't open the lid and she bangs and bangs and bangs, but the attic room is too high up and nobody ever goes up there because the owners have said there's a ghost. So, all the others search the house but she's never found. She bangs and bangs and bangs... and when the banging stops... she slowly rots away in the old chest.

There is a pause.

DOM: That's not the one I was thinking of.

WES: Tell us yours then. King of Spooky Tales.

DOM: It was about a woman down our street. They'd been doing lots of roadworks outside her house and repairing the pavement and all that. And this had made lots of dust. So, she was washing her windows, sitting on the window ledge.

JESS: Sitting on the window ledge?

DOM: Yes, sitting on the ledge, washing her windows, leaning out. And they were repairing the pavement below. She lost her balance and fell straight into a concrete mixer.

JESS: Concrete mixer?!

DREWEY: Coke anyone?

DOM: Drewey, we listened to yours.

WES: I'll have one, Drewey, thanks.

DOM: Everyone listened to Drewey's story.

DREWEY: My story was good. Good and scary.

DOM: Give it a chance. This is terrifying.

JESS: A concrete mixer, Dom?

DOM: Yes, she fell into a concrete mixer.

WES: The angle wouldn't be right.

JESS: Yeah.

KIA: What happened, Dom?

DOM: So anyway. She dies.

DREWEY: And it took fourteen blokes to lift her coffin!

DOM: It's not a joke, Drewey. This is true. Down our street.

JESS: What was her name?

DOM: Her name?

JESS: Yes. What was her name?

DOM: Mrs... Mrs... (*he looks around*) Tent... erly. Mrs Tenterly.

WES: Mrs Tenterly? Does she live next door to Mrs Sleeping Bagly?

DOM: Never mind what her name was. It's not important! The thing is now, down our street, loads of people have seen a ghost of a woman... but instead of a head... there's just... a block of concrete. How spooky is that?

DREWEY: That's the worst ghost story I've ever heard.

KIA: That would be pretty scary, if you saw a normal woman's body but with like this block of concrete head, coming towards you.

WES: Just push her over and she'd never be able to get up again!

KIA: What time is it?

DREWEY: It's nearly midnight.

KIA: Do you think Mum and Dad have gone to sleep, Wes?

WES: I'll have a look. All the lights in the house are off.

DREWEY: Listen.

KIA: What?

DREWEY: Quiet, isn't it? I'd say it was too quiet. The kind of quiet that happens just before midnight. The kind of quiet that there is just before something terrifying happens.

KIA: Stop it, Drew.

DREWEY: Something terrifying, that happens to four kids sleeping out in Wes' garden... with no parents around... and nobody to hear them scream.

JESS: That's not funny, Drewey. You know how freaked out Kia gets.

WES: Four? Drewey, you said something terrifying was about to happen to four kids.

DOM: Yeah. There are five of us.

DREWEY: No, you're wrong. There are four kids and one flesh-eating zombie! Aaaaaaahh!! (*she goes to attack the others*)

WES: Drewey, you squashed my Fruit and Nut, you twit. Chocolate all over my sleeping bag.

KIA: I think I'm going to go back into the house now.

WES: You can't. You'll wake up Mum and Dad.

DOM: Let your little sister go, if she's scared.

JESS: Since when have you been so brave, Dom.

DOM: What do you mean?

JESS: When we turned all the lights out at my house, you freaked out. Had to leave the room.

DOM: I thought it was a kissy game. That's all. I thought it was a kissy game or something and everybody was going to chase round and... and kiss.

DREWEY: Who'd want to kiss you? Kia can't leave because we haven't had the adventure yet.

KIA: I told you all I'd sleep out in the garden, but I'm not going out. We're not allowed out of the garden. Mum and Dad would go mad.

DREWEY: Only to the old house at the back.

WES: Not again, Drewey. You go on about this every time you come round here.

DREWEY: Unless we go, we'll never know.

JESS: Know what?

DREWEY: If what they say is true. Why it's been deserted for so long. What happened to the people who lived there. Why you can hear a moaning sound coming from inside when you stand at the front gate and listen...

DOM: You can actually. I've heard that moaning sound.

WES: It's Kia. She's always moaning. You could hear her from over there.

KIA: I am not.

DREWEY: Kia, you don't have to come with us. You could stay here all on your own if you wanted to... all on your own. Listen. Did you hear that?

KIA: What?

DREWEY: Oh, maybe it was nothing. I thought I heard a strange sound.

KIA: You can't leave me on my own.

DREWEY: Let's all go then. It's midnight. We'd better go now or it'll be too late.

JESS: Too late.

DREWEY: The gate only opens to strangers at midnight, just for a short while. Enough for four kids and a zombie to slip through and then it will close again. At midnight, once a year, the night of the terrible happening...

DREWEY: And tonight just so happens to be that night.

DOM: We've got to finish these crisps, they're Prawn Cocktail flavour. Jess, your favourite?

JESS: Time to go then. Wes?

WES: I'll go if you and Drewey are going.

DOM: I've got some mint Aeros somewhere. They must be at the bottom of my sleeping bag or something. We've nowhere near finished this midnight feast.

DREWEY: It's a different kind of midnight feast we'll be going to, Dom. The zombie, vampire, werewolf feast of flesh and blood. A feast of horror.

JESS: Drewey, pack it in. Let's just go and have a look around, have a laugh and come back.

WES: Let's do it!

DOM: Well, I'm not staying here.

KIA: Please don't go, please don't go. Seriously, I mean seriously. (*the others are creeping out of the tent*) Well I'm not going. I'm really not going you lot. Hey, wait for me!

They crawl out of the tent and stand in the night air.

DREWEY: A full moon. It's perfect, just perfect. All the signs have come together to tell us this is the right night. The date is right, the full moon, the midnight hour.

DOM: The smell of prawn cocktail on everyone's breath.

WES: Lift the side gate latch, very slowly. Don't let it creak and wake up Mum and Dad.

JESS does so. She pushes the gate open and everyone goes through. They move in a very tight group.

JESS: There's nobody in the street.

KIA: Seriously, guys, I mean seriously, can we go back to the tent. We're going to get into such big trouble.

DOM: The gate! The gate of the old deserted house is open!

DREWEY: It's a sign!

WES: It's always open. It's nearly falling off.

JESS: But the door...

They all now see what JESS is looking at.

DOM: The door is open. Wes, the door of the house is open.

WES: The door is never open. Kia, have you ever seen the door of the house open?

KIA: No. Seriously. No.

WES: Neither have I. Anybody?

DREWEY: The spirits have spoken. We must enter.

DOM: No way! No way! No way am I going in that house.

JESS: Afraid we're going to play kissy games, Dom?

DREWEY: Come on. Let's go inside.

They slowly move forward into the house, shining their torches around.

DOM: Hello. Is anybody there?

WES: Dom. Don't be stupid. It's a deserted house.

JESS: Look, the old wallpaper is peeling off the walls. There's still coat hooks. What's in there, Wes?

WES: (*he pushes a door and lets it swing back*) Nothing. Just an old fireplace. Some newspaper in the corner.

DREWEY: Whatever is living here at the moment won't come out straight away. It will wait until we're not expecting it. There is certainly something within the house. I can sense it, but right now it is hiding... in the darkest corners, behind the wallpaper, under the floorboards. There may be one. There maybe more than one. Who knows. Just waiting. Waiting for the right moment. (*pause*) Shall we go up the stairs?

DOM: I don't think I'd like to do that. I'm quite happy just here. Or maybe outside, or maybe back in the tent, or in my own home, in my own bed.

WES: With your own teddy bear.

DOM: Well are you going up there?

JESS: We're all going up there.

They take a deep breath. They climb up the stairs, by walking on the spot, shining their torches around, they notice things caught in the beam of the torch.

JESS: An old picture of a woman. Still on the wall.

DREWEY: Her eyes are following us.

WES: An old jumper or something, in the corner over there.

DREWEY: They had to leave in a hurry.

JESS: (*pushing a door*) Another old fireplace. A small one in the bedroom.

DREWEY: Still glowing hot after all these years. Keeping the spirits warm.

WES: Another old newspaper in the corner.

DREWEY: Telling of the dreadful fate...

DOM: OK, OK, Drewey. That's enough. We've done it now. We've looked around. There's nothing more to prove. We can go.

WES: Look, you lot. More stairs. They must go up to an attic room.

KIA: Attic room? I'm so frightened now. Can one of you take me back? I'd really like it if one of you took me back now.

DREWEY: Just as soon as we've seen the attic room.

DOM: (*talking to himself*) Here we are climbing the attic stairs of the spooky deserted house and I'm thinking about happy things like Christmas and holidays and it not being dark and scary. Don't make me look in the attic, Drewey, don't make me look in the attic.

JESS: Dom, we'll just take one quick look and then all go back to the tent.

DOM: Promise?

JESS: Promise.

DOM: Don't tell anyone I was scared, will you.

JESS: You're not scared, Dom.

DOM: No, of course not.

DREWEY: Oh no. Oh no. It can't be. Don't look, don't look in the corner.

DOM: (*banging the torch to try to make it work*) My torch. My torch has gone.

JESS: Mine too. What is it, Drewey?

WES: I've seen it, Drewey. Look you two. Look. Where I'm shining my torch.

JESS: A chest. A big old Victorian chest, like the one in the story. In an attic room.

DREWEY: But look, look at the lid.

ALL: Aaaaagh!!!

They start running and bumping into each other. Kia is 'lost' amongst the panicking crowd. She always finds herself behind the others, whichever way they turn.

DOM: The lid. The lid's opening! Go, go, go, let's get out.

WES: The rotting woman, she's coming out. She's coming for us.

JESS: Where's Kia?

DREWEY: Where's Kia?

DOM: Where's Kia?

WES: The rotting woman has got Kia and she's dragging her into the chest and she'll shut the lid.

DOM: We've lost Kia forever!

WES: Mum and Dad will kill me.

DREWEY: Get out. She'll drag us in too.

DOM: Out the door, out the door, out the door, quick!

They break through to the outside.

JESS: Come on quick. Back to the tent.

WES: (*over his shoulder to see if anything is coming*) Lift the latch slowly, Jess. We don't want to wake...

JESS: I think your screaming will have woken everyone up.

WES: I wasn't screaming. (*they stand for a moment out of breath*) My little sister. We've lost Kia forever.

KIA: I'm here. I was with you all the time.

WES: Well why didn't you say so?

KIA: I was so scared I couldn't speak.

JESS: Come on, let's get back in the tent.

They crawl back into the tent. Pause.

KIA: I'm tired now, Wes. No more stories. Can we get to sleep?

JESS: Yeah. Come on.

They all get in sleeping bags, plump pillows, lie down.

DOM: Let's forget it now. Stupid old house, not going to scare us.

WES: Night everyone.

ALL OTHERS: Night.

WES: Yeah, night.

JESS: Let's get some sleep now. Night everybody.

There is a pause. After a moment.

DOM: Did you really see that lid lift up, Drewey?

DREWEY: I thought I did... yes, I did... it definitely lifted up. And I think I just saw a hand...

Pause. At exactly the same time they all sit bolt upright, eyes wide open, terrified.

A SWAGGER AND A SNARL

Characters:

JAYNA	girl, aged 13-14
SHONA	girl, same age
TYRONE	boy, aged 13-14
LEE	boy, same age

The action is played in an empty space but for two chairs. When the focus is not on a character, they freeze in a strong position or turn their back to the audience. JAYNA and SHONA are sitting. SHONA has a pen pressed hard into JAYNA's leg. LEE and TYRONE are standing. TYRONE has LEE pinned at arm's length, gripping his throat.

JAYNA: Shona has the point of a pen pressed hard into my leg. We're in a Science class and I want to scream. But I can't.

LEE: Tyrone has his hand tight around my throat and it hurts. Up against a wall, in the corridor, and I want to breath. But I can't.

SHONA looks around her to make sure nobody is looking, as she says...

SHONA: If you tell on me, your life will be total misery. Understand? Total misery.

JAYNA nods and continues to face front, where the 'class' is being taught.

JAYNA: You're hurting my leg.

SHONA: Quiet. Do you know why I left my last school?

JAYNA: No.

SHONA: You don't want to know. Believe me, you do not want to know.

JAYNA: I don't think I want to know.

SHONA: Good.

TYRONE looks around him to make sure that nobody is coming, as he says...

TYRONE: Day one. Let's get some rules straight. I don't like you and you don't like me. Agreed?

LEE: Oh yes. Agreed. Very much agreed.

TYRONE: You being cheeky?

LEE: No, I'm just agreeing with you, Tyrone.

TYRONE: Don't you be cheeky. You'll cry for your mum when I've finished with you. Better do it now. Go on then. Do it.

LEE: (*in a weak voice*) Mum. (*to the audience*) It is Tyrone's first day at our school. (*to Tyrone*) Could you just loosen your grip a minute? I'm trying to speak.

TYRONE: All right. Tell 'em. I'm not letting go, but you can speak.

LEE: Thanks. (*he continues to the audience*) Yeah, so it's Tyrone's first day at our school and Mrs Thorn asked me to look after him... show him around. And Tyrone says...

TYRONE: Thanks, Mrs Thorn. I'll stick by Lee all day and won't let him out of my sight.

LEE: It was me. I was chosen. It could have been anyone in the class, but I was chosen. And pretty soon Tyrone says he wants to go to the toilet, and Mrs Thorn asked me to show him where it is, and we walked down the corridor together, we turn a corner and suddenly I'm pinned against a wall.

TYRONE does this.

TYRONE: Day one. Let's get some rules straight...

LEE: Tyrone... Tyrone. They've seen that bit.

TYRONE: Oh, yeah. Where were we?

LEE: "Don't be cheeky."

TYRONE: What?! (*he looks like he is going to hit LEE*)

LEE: No, no. You were telling me not to be cheeky, remember?

TYRONE: Oh yeah. Don't be cheeky.

He puts LEE in a tight grip again and the focus returns to SHONA and JAYNA.

SHONA: You're going to be my friend, Jayna. You're going to help me with my homework and all sorts of friendly things. You're lucky. You were chosen.

JAYNA: Chosen?

SHONA: Yeah, Mr Donnely asked you to look after me, remember? New girl, needs a buddy, a friend to show her around, to look after her. Today you were lucky. It was you.

JAYNA: You're really hurting me, Shona. There's blood and ink on my leg. (*to the audience*) She is really hurting me, here. The point of the pen has gone in and there is actually blood on my leg. Do you know what else I'm thinking? I'm thinking: I nearly didn't come to school today. I've got a bit of a cold and my mum said "Are you sure you are OK to go to school?" and I told her that I had to get in because we've got this Science test today. I thought I wouldn't be able to concentrate because I would be coughing all the time. But instead I haven't been able to concentrate because the new girl is pushing her pen into my leg. I haven't coughed once. Which I suppose is good.

SHONA: Lucky I don't tattoo you. Scratch 'Shona' with a pen. So you've got me forever. Shall I stop it now?

JAYNA: Yes!

SHONA: Yes, what?

JAYNA: Yes please, Shona.

SHONA takes the pen off JAYNA's leg.

SHONA: So, what's the answer to Question 2?

JAYNA: It's 'b) Bacteria'. 'Which of the following can be harmful and poison the human system?' It's b), Shona. You need to write 'Bacteria'.

They continue to work and the focus shifts back again. TYRONE releases his grip on LEE.

TYRONE: Want some gum?

LEE: Not in school.

TYRONE: Take it. (*he is more forceful*) Take it!

LEE: Thanks. (*he takes some and puts it in his pocket*)

TYRONE: Turn out your pockets.

LEE: What?

TYRONE: I want to see what you've got in your pockets.

LEE: Only this. (*he produces the gum*)

TYRONE: That's my gum. Have you been stealing from me?

LEE: But you gave it...

TYRONE: Thief. What a thief. Give it back. Give it back now.

LEE: (*to the audience*) I think today is going to be the longest day of my life.

TYRONE: The other pocket. Show me what's in the other pocket.

LEE: (*showing TYRONE*) It's my dinner money.

TYRONE: Whose money?

LEE: But I need to buy something to eat.

TYRONE: Whose money?

LEE: Yours?

TYRONE: Quick learner, Lee. You're a quick learner.

TYRONE holds out his hand. After a pause LEE puts his money in it.

LEE: (*to the audience*) The longest day...

The two scenes dissolve. JAYNA talks to the audience.

JAYNA: I went to find Lee at lunch time, because I knew he'd been asked to look after Shona's brother and I suspected that he had been making new friends in the same way as I had.

LEE: (*to the audience*) We told each other what had happened. Which we'll make shorter now, because I think you've already got the idea.

JAYNA: (*to LEE*) Shona's going to make my life miserable. Blood and ink. Here. (*she holds her leg*)

LEE: Tyrone's going to make me cry for my mum. Hand here, on my throat.

BOTH: Nightmare.

JAYNA: You didn't, did you?

LEE: What?

JAYNA: Cry for your mum.

LEE: No, of course not. (*he looks out to the audience for support*) Well, what would you do?

JAYNA: We agreed that what we should try to do was avoid Shona and Tyrone. Just keep out of their way.

All four move around the space. SHONA and TYRONE are searching for the other two. LEE and JAYNA are keeping out of their way - moving down corridors, turning corners - dodging, hiding, swerving.

LEE: Which is easier said than done. But these are the things we tried.

JAYNA: One. Go straight to your next lesson and don't hang around the corridors.

LEE: Two. Don't ever go to the toilets. It's a death trap leading to a watery grave.

JAYNA: Ever?

LEE: Ever.

JAYNA: Three. Take the long way home if you know it's going to be safer.

LEE: Four. Don't bring in dinner money, anything to eat, anything to drink, any coat, football or possession of any kind.

SHONA: (*suddenly meeting JAYNA. Others freeze.*) My pencil case. I think that's my pencil case now.

They move again - the avoiding movement.

JAYNA: If you've got to bring stuff in, put your name on everything: ruler, rubber, pencils... everything.

LEE: Five. Don't make eye contact. Never look directly at them, it's inviting trouble.

LEE: Six. In fact, keep your eyes down at all times. But try not to bump into things.

JAYNA and LEE bump into each other and are shocked.

LEE: I'm really sorry, don't hit me! Oh, it's you.

They continue their movement, illustrating what they are saying.

JAYNA: Seven. Even think yourself invisible.

LEE: (*creeping around*) I'm so small and insignificant. There's nobody here at all.

JAYNA: Nothing to bother about... just invisible me.

TYRONE: (*finds LEE*) What do you think you're doing? Creepy boy. I'm supposed to take this book to the library. But you can do it, can't you?

SHONA: (*finds JAYNA*) There you are, my best friend. I need some more answers from you, for last night's homework.

LEE: And the last thing we tried...

The rushing movement stops.

JAYNA: Eight. Give up. Our lives are miserable.

LEE: I've not eaten properly for a week.

JAYNA: I'm exhausted. It takes me twice as long to get home and all day I'm running round corridors...

LEE: ...head down, bumping into things.

JAYNA: When I close my eyes at night, I see Shona as a hooded witch hovering over my bed.

LEE: When I close my eyes at night, I see Tyrone like a devil monster, screaming in my face.

JAYNA: And my guts are all knotted.

LEE: And my head is like lead.

JAYNA: We haven't done anything to deserve this. But what can you do?

LEE: Better creep off, better be invisible. (*pause*) Why do you think they do it?

TYRONE and SHONA come to the centre of the space. JAYNA and LEE represent their victims.

SHONA: Our reign of terror began on that first day.

TYRONE: You better do this.

SHONA: You better do that.

TYRONE: Or else.

SHONA: Or else.

TYRONE: We walk down corridors with a swagger and a snarl.

SHONA: And all the tiddlers, the weaklings, the runts, part to make way. We are the bosses of the school. Everybody must know. I give them killer looks and other kids wither before me.

TYRONE: I barge and charge and bruise and bark. And soon they will gather around to be our 'friends'. With a...

SHONA: "You tell them, Tyrone." And...

TYRONE: "We think you're brilliant, Shona."

SHONA: And if those teachers try to tell us off... We say... It's not fair.

TYRONE: It wasn't me.

SHONA: You're just picking on us for no reason. (*pause*). But we're not going to get done by the teachers because nobody will dare say a word against us, 'cause they know what might happen. Don't they?

Pause. JAYNA and LEE speak to the audience.

JAYNA & LEE: It's Friday.

JAYNA: We survived another week. We are in the playground and I'm thinking that after today I won't have to see Shona and Tyrone for two whole days. But right now Shona is making me teach her how to download stuff onto her mobile phone.

SHONA: (*to JAYNA*) And I want to download all the best ring tones and pictures. Show me how to do it so I can be faster than everyone else.

LEE: I'm standing against a wall, head down, trying to look invisible and feeling miserable, thinking about Tyrone. Some boys are playing football near to me and the ball rolls my way.

JAYNA: "Oi, Lee. Kick it back!" they shouted.

LEE: And all the horrible feelings, all the sneaking about, all that feeling scared, sort of bubbled up.

JAYNA: And I'm standing with Shona's mobile and all of her hurting and spiteful words and demanding, demanding, demanding I do things for her started that knot in my guts…

LEE: "Oi, Lee. Kick it back!" they shouted again and I kicked that ball as hard as I possibly could. I kicked it with a shout, "Take that, Tyrone!"

JAYNA: And the ball shot through the air just as Tyrone walked round the corner onto the playground. And I shouted "No!" and dropped Shona's mobile phone.

TYRONE: Thwack! Right in the face. My skull knocked back upon my thick bull-neck. Knocked dizzy, brain rattled. With the words… "Take that, Tyrone!" echoing round my head. I crumpled down, knees gone, folding to the ground, joint by joint.

LEE stands and watches TYRONE with total horror.

JAYNA: Everybody in the playground gasped and stood completely still. All eyes on Tyrone. Except for me. I looked down at Shona's mobile. Put my foot on it and pushed down hard, until I heard a 'crunch'. Lee! Lee!

LEE stops staring at TYRONE, looks across at JAYNA and then the mobile phone. Pause.

Lee? Run?

LEE: Run!

They run off the space.